YOU NEED HELP,
CHARLIE BROWN

Books by Charles M. Schulz

Peanuts®

More Peanuts®

Good Grief, More Peanuts®!

Good Ol' Charlie Brown

Snoopy

You're Out of Your Mind, Charlie Brown!

But We Love You, Charlie Brown

Peanuts® Revisited

Go Fly a Kite, Charlie Brown

Peanuts® Every Sunday

It's a Dog's Life, Charlie Brown

You Can't Win, Charlie Brown

Snoopy, Come Home

You Can Do It, Charlie Brown

We're Right Behind You, Charlie Brown

As You Like It, Charlie Brown

Sunday's Fun Day, Charlie Brown

You Need Help, Charlie Brown

Snoopy and The Red Baron

The Unsinkable Charlie Brown

You'll Flip, Charlie Brown

You're Something Else, Charlie Brown

Weekly Reader Books presents

YOU NEED HELP, CHARLIE BROWN

A NEW *PEANUTS* BOOK

by Charles M. Schulz

Selected Cartoons from
YOU NEED HELP, CHARLIE BROWN

HOLT, RINEHART AND WINSTON

New York · Chicago · San Francisco

This book is a presentation of Weekly Reader Books.
Weekly Reader Books offers book clubs for children from
preschool to young adulthood. All quality hardcover books are selected
by a distinguished Weekly Reader Selection Board.

For further information write to:
Weekly Reader Books
1250 Fairwood Ave.
Columbus, Ohio 43216

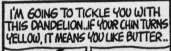

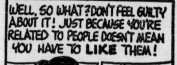

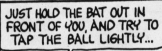

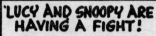

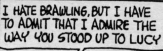

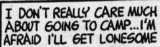

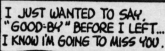

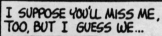

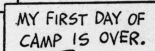

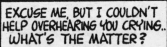

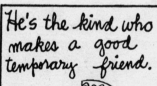

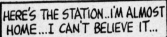

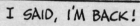

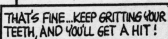

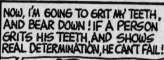

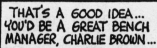

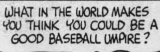

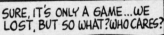

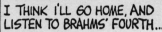

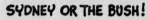

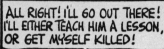

WHY DID YOU WRITE, "CHARLIE BROWN IS A BLOCKHEAD" ON THE SIDEWALK?

BECAUSE I SINCERELY BELIEVE YOU ARE A BLOCKHEAD! I HAVE TO WRITE WHAT I BELIEVE IS TRUE.. IT'S MY MORAL RESPONSIBILITY!

DEEP DOWN I ADMIRE HER INTEGRITY..

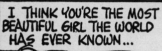

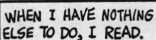

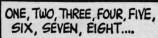